Understanding Grey:

A Personal Story of Autism and Loss

by

Mike Barbour

DORRANCE
PUBLISHING CO
EST. 1920
PITTSBURGH, PENNSYLVANIA 15238

Dorrance Publishing Co
585 Alpha Drive
Pittsburgh, PA 15238
Visit our website at *www.dorrancebookstore.com*

ISBN: 978-1-6366-1497-7
eISBN: 978-1-6366-1676-6

Understanding Grey will help autistic individuals understand loss.

Temple Grandin, Author
Thinking in Pictures

Understanding Grey captures life, loss and love as only a person with autism can see it. This heartrending story recounts the friendship of two young men with disabilities living together enriching one another's lives. Ian and Matt serve a beautiful example of what it means to color someone's world and see each other as God intended. When tragedy cuts their friendship short, the story takes on unexpected poignancy and joy. Their experience is something we can all learn from. Life is too short not to read this book. A must read for all parents.

Don and Karen Arias
Parents and Autism Advocates

This story of love and loss is poignant and deceptively simple. Ian shows us all a genuine "celebration of life" in the midst of his grief. The illustrations are just right. Engaging and fun; mournfully grey. Take a long look at this short story that encapsulates so much.

Nancy E. Mills, LCSW

Dedicated to

Ian — Thank you for the many lessons you have taught me

Anita — Who shared Matt with the world

Pam McDonough — A devoted caregiver and friend

Matt — Pure love that never fades

Understanding Grey:

A Personal Story of Autism and Loss

My name is Ian, and I live with autism.

I usually view the world in black and white,

but some things in life are grey. Changes in routines, people,

places, and emotions confuse me.

Understanding and accepting these types of changes

can take weeks, months, and even years.

I met my best friend, Matt, when I was ten years old.

He was the coolest guy I had ever known.

Matt helped me to see the world in color.

As friends, Matt and I made each other laugh. His world on wheels amazed me, and I loved him.

We joined sports groups with other guys, shared family dinners, and sometimes just spent special moments together.

Over time, we became men and roommates.

Every morning was music time and I danced.

Matt laughed so much—he loved these mornings.

His disability had taken his voice, but he spoke clearer to me than anyone ever had. We sometimes wore crazy shirts and acted silly and goofy together.

Let's Rock!

Matt understood and believed in me.

He was just an incredible human being.

Matt got sick and needed surgery, but he didn't get better and he didn't come home.

It was the greyest of grey days.

People talked to me like I understood. I couldn't tell them how much my heart hurt.

There was a service held for Matt, but he wasn't there. One of our favorite songs was played. Most people cried, but I…

Let's Rock!

DANCED

Most of all, I remember his beautiful smiling face. He gave me so much laughter and joy. Matt made every day better. No one could take that away. Those memories fill me with happiness and will stay with me forever.

You would be so lucky to find a friend like Matt to color your world.

Notes About Autism

Autism is a spectrum disorder (ASD), in that the characteristic symptoms present differently in individuals. The outcome of the disorder can be mild to severe. Much has been written about autism, but for the purpose of this story, the focus is on the individual's social awkwardness and/or social disconnectedness from others. Since these people often have difficulty identifying social cues, they are most frequently literal in their thinking and understanding of the world around them. So, abstract concepts like love and death are difficult for them to understand and accept.

Autism spectrum disorder. CDC.gov. April 2021.

Autism Spectrum Disorder. nimh.nih.gov. Retrieved March 2021.

Grandin, T. (1996). Thinking in pictures and other reports from my life with autism. Vintage Books: New York.

Supportive Living Homes

Supported living homes are a residential option for many individuals with mild to severe disabilities. This living arrangement allows individuals to choose how and with whom they will live. Supported living affords people with disabilities the opportunity to have their own home, make life choices and to subsequently increase their independence. The Florida services are funded through the Medicaid waiver program, but the concept has been adopted in many other states across the country.

Grandin, T. & Moore, D. (2015). The loving push. Future Horizons: Arlington, Texas.

Supported living. apd.myflorida.com. 2021.

CPSIA information can be obtained
at www.ICGtesting.com
Printed in the USA
BVHW022154170422
634392BV00002B/31